20 beans

C000201909

A person to play with, and small objects such as dried beans, peas, pasta shapes or small Lego bri

Each guess what 20 beans looks like, and try to take that many without counting.

Lee 18   Jay 24

Now each count your beans by grouping them in 2s.

Write down how many you took. Who was closest? That person scores a point.

Play until one person has 3 points.

Together count exactly 20, put them in a small bag and bring them into school.

In class You can play the game in class, with the children in pairs.

In order

Ordering

4   5   9   12   2   6   10   11

Look at these cards. Write the numbers in order from largest to smallest.

Choose your favourite number and write it large. Turn it into a picture.

In class Discuss the order, using real cards or the number line.

Heads or tails?

A person to play with, small objects such as counters or dried pasta shapes, and a coin

Take turns to flip the coin.
For heads, take 2 counters.
For tails, take 3 counters.

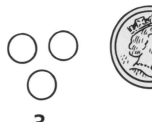

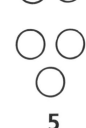

Write down the number
you take. Each time
add more counters
to your pile and write down the new number.

3

5

Keep playing until one of you has 10 – the winner.

Parent's note Encourage the child not to count the counters they already have, but to count on from that number: 'I have 5, I take 2 more, that's 6, 7.'

In class You can play this in class, you against the whole group.

Lollies

Choose 2 lollies. Write
down their prices and add
them together.

$$5p + 1p = 6p$$

Repeat this until you have
done 6 additions.

Choose 3 lollies. How much
would it cost to buy all 3?

In class Draw the lollies on the board and discuss
which ones the children chose. Discuss how to add 3.

How many left?

A person to play with, a coin and 10 small objects each such as dried pasta shapes or counters

Each start with 10 counters, and write down 10.

Take turns to flip the coin. For heads, take away 2 counters. For tails, take away 1 counter. Before you take it away, say how many you will have left.

10 take away 2 leaves 8.

Write down the subtraction.

$$10 - 2 = 8$$

The first player to get rid of all their counters wins. You must have exactly the right 'flip' to finish.

In class Play the game in class, pairing a child who has played it at home with a child who has not.

Buy the toys

7p

11p

12p

8p

Choose coins to buy each toy. Draw or write the coins you would need for each.

In class Draw the 12p toy on the board and discuss how many ways there are to buy it.

Snakes and ladders

 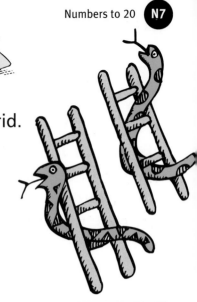

A person to play with, a number grid (I to 20), a counter each and a dice

Draw your own snakes and ladders on the grid.

Each place a counter at 'start'. Take turns to throw the dice, and move your counter a matching number of spaces.

If you land on the bottom of a ladder, climb up to the top. If you land on the head of a snake, slide down to the tail.

In class You can play this in class, you against the whole group.

House numbers

A person to help

Walk along a street together and look at how the houses are numbered.

Count in 2s with your partner, taking turns to say each number.

Draw a street of your own and number the houses.

In class Make a street for the classroom wall, with doors numbered in 2s.

Number triangles

 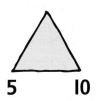

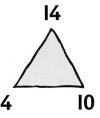
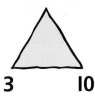
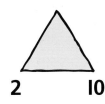

Copy the triangles. Add the 2 numbers at the bottom to find the missing number at the top of each triangle.
Write in the missing numbers.

> **In class** Draw some large triangles on the board. Ask children to stick number cards on to match the homework.

Stars

A person to play with, a handful of counters and some small objects such as Lego bricks or coins

Cover the numbers with bricks. Take turns to choose a number between 5 and 10 and hold up a matching number of fingers.

Tell your partner which brick to lift, and fold down fingers to match the number.

Count how many fingers are left held up and then take a matching number of counters.

Play 3 rounds each. Who has the most counters?

> **In class** Play in teams, putting numbers on the board and Blu-tacking a piece of card over each one.

Balloons

Copy all the balloons. Colour only the ones that have 2 numbers that add up to 5.

In class Draw a 'hidden' letter picture on the board, and have the children come and shade the parts where the two numbers add to 5 to reveal the letter.

Add 10

A person to play with, and a handful of counters

Cover each star number with a counter. Take turns to lift a counter.

Add 10 to the number and write down the total. Your partner checks it. If you are correct, keep the counter.

Keep playing like this until all the counters have been taken. Who has the most?

In class Play the game in class, with the children in pairs.

Choose a coin

A person to play with, and a handful of small change

Put the coins on the table. Choose a coin each.

How could you give someone the value of your coin without giving them that coin?

Draw your chosen coin and how you made the value.

1p and 1p

In class Discuss the different ways they found of making each value.

Robot for sale

A person to play with, and a handful of small change

What coins could you use to buy the robot? Your coins must equal exactly 10p. Choose a different way of making 10p each, and draw or write your coins.

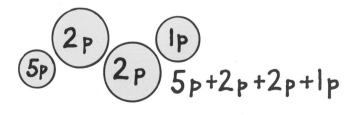

5p + 2p + 2p + 1p

10p

Try and find at least 2 different ways each.

In class Draw a large robot marked '10p' on the board. Ask the children to suggest ways of buying it.

A spoonful

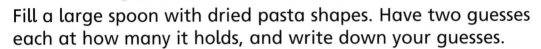
A person to talk to, a large spoon and small objects such as dried pasta shapes or beans

Fill a large spoon with dried pasta shapes. Have two guesses each at how many it holds, and write down your guesses.

Count the shapes by grouping them in 2s. Write down the actual number. Whose guess was closest?

In class Ask the children to estimate the number of pasta shapes in a tea cup, then count them.

Comic prices

Place-value **N16**

A person to talk to, and some 10p and 1p coins

Take turns to choose a comic. Draw the correct number of 10p and 1p coins you need to buy it.

Draw a comic you like, or write its name. Write its price.

In class Discuss which coins they need to buy the comics they chose. Make a catalogue of their pictures and prices, from cheapest to most expensive.

Double planets

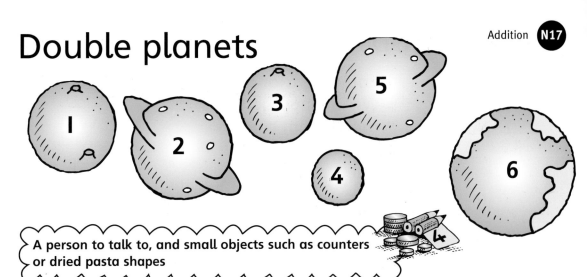

A person to talk to, and small objects such as counters or dried pasta shapes

Place a counter on each planet.
Take turns to remove a counter.

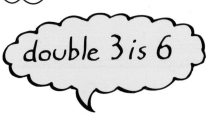

double 3 is 6

Read the number and double it, using your fingers to help you. Say the double and take that many counters.

When all the planets are uncovered, who has the most counters?

In class Make some planet numbers and hang moons by them with the doubles on, to help the children remember them.

Card pairs

A person to help you, and paper or card such as the backs of old birthday cards

Make these number cards.

Arrange them in pairs so that each pair adds up to 6.

Stick the pairs together so that the front and back add up to 6. Decorate your cards.

Triangle tops

9

Copy the triangle.
Write 2 numbers at
the bottom corners
that add up to 9.

Draw at least 4 more
different triangles
with 9 at the top.

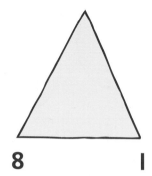

8   1

In class Discuss the triangles. Draw all the possible triangles on the board.

Make 10

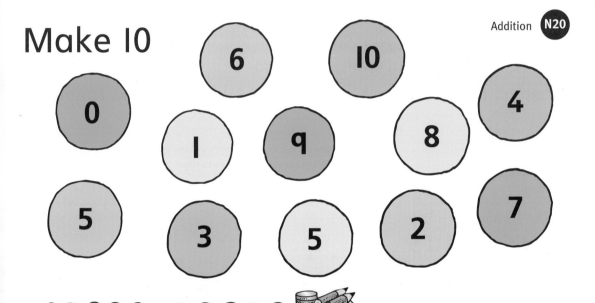

A person to play with, and small objects such as counters or dried pasta shapes

Cover the numbers with counters. Take turns to lift 2 counters.

If the 2 numbers add to 10, keep the counters. If not, put them back on their numbers.

In class Play the game in class with the children in pairs, using 0–10 number cards face down.

Falling off

A person to play with, a coin and a counter each

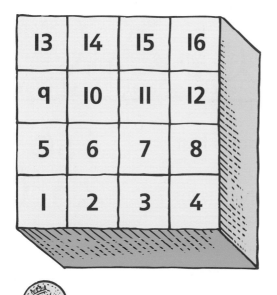

Each place a counter on 'I'. Flip a coin. For heads, move one space to the right. For tails, move one space up.

If you land on an even number, take a counter. If you land on an odd number, do not take a counter.

Keep playing until someone falls off the edge. Who has the most counters?

In class The children can draw different grids and play again.

Guess the total

A person to play with, and a dice

Suppose you throw the dice twice. What different totals can you get? Choose a total each.

Take turns to throw the dice twice. Add the 2 numbers.

If you throw your chosen total, you get a point. Play until someone has 3 (or 5) points.

It might be 7

It could be 9

In class Play in class with the children. Discuss which total was the best to choose.

Who came first?

cat | dog | snake | rabbit | fish

Look at the animals. Which animal is first?
Write or draw it.

Which is second? Keep going. Which is last?

1st
2nd

In class Say the position, such as 'fifth'. The children say which animal is fifth.

Comparing numbers

6

8

A person to play with, counters and 1–10 number cards

Shuffle the cards and spread them out face down. Take a
card each.

Who has the smaller number? That person takes a counter.

Keep taking a card each until the cards have all gone.
Who has the most counters?

In class Play in class in pairs, or as a 'class against teacher' game.

Change from 10p

 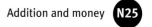

You are going to buy each sweet. You pay with a 10p coin each time.

Write down how much change you get each time.

Guess how much all the sweets would cost together.

In class The children can discuss how to work out a grand total.

Make the number

A person to play with, number cards 4–10 and some counters

Spread the cards out face down.

Take turns to choose a card. Make that number by adding 2 smaller numbers.

Write down your addition. If it is correct, take the card. If not, turn the card back over.

Keep playing until all the cards have gone. Who has the most cards? Play again.

In class Discuss which numbers can be made in the most ways.

Subtraction spider

8 – 1

8 – 8

8 – 7

8 – 6

8 – 5

8 – 0

8 – 2

8 – 3

Copy and complete the subtractions.

In class Repeat the activity using a beetle with 6 legs.

Cover the number

A person to play with, and several counters (one colour each)

Choose a 1-digit number. Count in 10s from that number beyond 100.

The other person puts a counter on the numbers on the grid that they hear you say. Then swap.

Carry on playing.

When all the numbers are covered, who has put the most counters on the grid?

98	61	40	16
59	10	11	12
36	95	77	24
42	28	33	19

In class Put a grid on the board and do some counting in 10s, choosing a grid number to start the count.

Add 10

 65

28

 39

17

 42

33

 75

Write the card numbers. Add 10 to each number and write the answer.

In class The children can give each other a number and then reply with the number 10 more.

Computer games

A person to play with

Choose a screen and write down the score. Your helper takes away 10 and writes down the new score. Now swap.

Keep going until all the screens have been chosen. Each add up all your new scores. The winner is the one with the largest score.

In class Discuss which 3 screens give the best score.

Seeing stars

A person to play with, and several Lego bricks

Cover each star with a brick. Remove a brick. Say the number that adds to the star number to make 10.

Write down the number you say. This is your score.

Now swap. Carry on playing until all the stars are uncovered.

Add up your scores. Who has the largest total?

In class Play in class, teacher versus children.

Add them up

Copy the grid. Add the 2 numbers in each row and write the answers in the space on the right.

Add the 2 numbers in each column and write the answers in the spaces below.

Try adding the two answers along the bottom, and the two answers down the side. What do you notice?

In class Draw another similar grid on the board. Let the children experiment with other grids.

One more

A person to play with, a dice and lots of counters or Lego bricks

Throw the dice and write down the number. Write the number 1 more than that number.

Add the 2 numbers and take a matching number of counters.

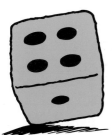

$$4 + 5 = 9$$

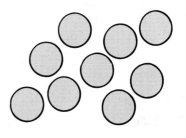

Swap, and keep playing until one person has 40 counters.

In class Play a similar game with children choosing a card (1 to 10).

Team shirts

Choose either even or odd numbers to be your team.
Write down the numbers you have chosen.

In class Discuss which numbers are even and which are odd. What is the largest odd number here? What is the largest even number here?

Give me five

Numbers to 100 **N35**

A person to help

Take turns to count in 5s. Show a hand for each number you say. 5, 10, 15, 20 ... Count as far as you can.

Look for an example of a 5s number you have seen around your home. Write down the example you find.

In class Discuss which examples the children chose. How do we know they fit into our 5s count?

Find the page

A person to play with, a book and some counters

Choose a rosette. Say the number. Your partner has to find that page in the book.

If they are correct, they get a counter. Now swap.

Keep playing until all the rosettes have been chosen.
How many counters do you each have?

In class As you send the children out to play, count the 1st child to go out, the 2nd child, etc.

Add 5

Add 5 to each card number in turn, writing the addition.

Make up a card number of your own and add 5 to it.

In class Discuss what answers they would get if they added 6 to each card number.

Cover the planets

A person to play with, 20 counters, a dice and 6 Lego bricks

In turn, take a handful of counters and count them, then throw a dice.

Take away counters to match the dice number, and count how many are left.

If that number is on a planet, cover it with a brick. Play until all the planets are covered.

> **In class** Discuss what numbers are good to throw if you start with 10 counters.

Subtract 10

  25 28 30

Subtract 10 from each card number. Write the subtraction, and the answer.

Write the card number that would give the answer 12.

$$23 - 10 =$$

> **In class** Discuss some harder subtractions, giving a child a number and asking them to say the number 10 less.

Cover the coins

 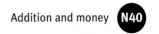

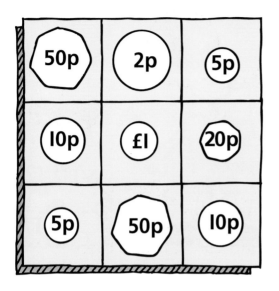

A person to play with, and some counters each

In turn, put a counter on a coin on the grid. Say some other coins that make the same amount.

Check with your partner. If you are correct, your counter stays. If not, take it off.

20p
10p and 10p

Keep playing until all the coins are covered. Who has the most counters on the grid?

In class Discuss the different ways of making each coin.

Take 2 coins

A person to play with, and some coins

Place a handful of coins on the table. Your partner shuts their eyes.

Take 2 coins. Your partner opens their eyes. They have to guess how much you have.

When they guess correctly, swap over. Keep on playing, sometimes taking 2 coins and sometimes taking 3. Tell your partner how many coins you have taken each time.

In class Discuss the different amounts you could have with just 2 coins.

Who is taller?

A person to help you

Choose 2 people or animals in your family. Who is taller? Who is shorter?

How much taller is the taller one? Draw both carefully, drawing the taller one taller and the shorter one shorter.

In class Discuss the heights of the two people or animals. Make a class book called 'taller' and a class book called 'shorter' in which to mount their pictures.

Measuring strip

A person to help you, a piece of card, crayons and scissors

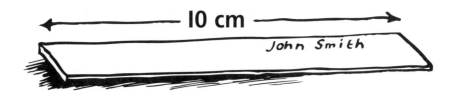

Make a 10 cm strip using a piece of card. Decorate it with your name.

Choose something to measure. Draw a picture of it.

How many strips long is it? How many strips wide is it?

In class Discuss the lengths of the different things they measure.

What's the time?

{ o'clock } { six } { three } { seven } { ten }

Write the time shown on each clock. Use the list of key words to help you.

In class Discuss what the children might be doing at each of the times shown.

TV programmes

A person to help you

What time is your favourite TV programme? Ask your helper to write down the time (to the nearest half hour).

half past five   half past three   10 o'clock

Write down your TV programme. Draw a clock showing that time on it.

In class Discuss and compare the different times.

A light meal

Look in the food cupboard. Find a tin or a heavy packet containing something that you like to eat. Draw it.

Find another packet of food that is lighter than this, also containing something that you like to eat. Draw that.

In class Discuss and compare the different packets drawn. Which one is the heaviest? Which one is the lightest of all?

Find a kilogram

A person to play with

Find something at home that you think weighs a kilogram. Look at different packets or weigh some different things to help you decide what to choose.

Draw your chosen object.

In class Discuss and compare the different things the children found. How did they choose them?

Diary day

| Monday | Tuesday | Wednesday | Thursday | Friday | Saturday | Sunday |

Look at the days of the week. Choose your favourite day.

Make a diary page for that day with a picture that shows why it is your favourite day. You can write a sentence as well if you like.

In class The children can discuss why they like their chosen day.

A big drink

A person to help, and 2 drinking containers such as a mug and a glass

Which one of these containers do you think holds the most drink?

Compare them by filling one with water and pouring it into the other. Repeat this the other way around.

Which holds the most? Draw both containers and colour the one that holds the most.

In class Discuss the different containers.

Sleep time

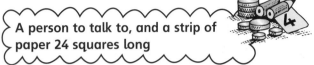

A person to talk to, and a strip of paper 24 squares long

How many hours do you sleep each night? Colour that number of squares on your strip of paper in dark blue or black.

How many hours do you spend eating? Colour that number of squares red.

How many hours do you spend playing? Colour that number of squares green. Colour the rest yellow.

How many hours are there in the day? Write it on the back of your strip.

In class Compare their strips. Who sleeps the longest? Who sleeps the least? Who spends the most time eating, and playing?

Seasons

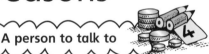

A person to talk to

Which is your favourite season?

Make a card of your favourite season, with a suitable picture on the front.

Write a greeting inside.

Happy Summer

Count the shapes

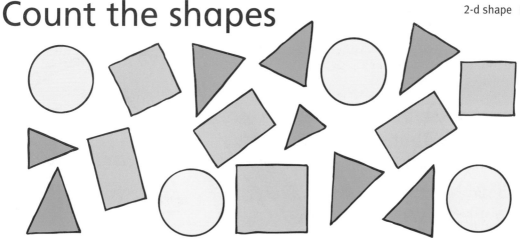

Count how many squares. Draw a square and write how many.

Do the same for triangles, rectangles and circles.

> **In class** Discuss how many of each shape there were. Choose a child to draw an example of each shape on the board.

Take a walk

Walk around 2 pieces of furniture in your house. Describe your route to your helper.

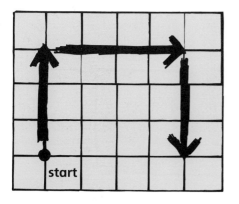

Say whether each turn is anticlockwise or clockwise. Ask your helper to help you draw your route.

> **In class** Choose some of the children's routes and draw these on the board. Talk the children round them.

Draw a cube

Look around your house. Can you find a cube? Draw it.
Be careful to draw it accurately.

In class Discuss their cubes. What did they find?

Dice shapes

A person to play with, and a dice

Take turns to throw the dice, and draw a shape with the
number of sides shown on the dice.

Compare your drawings. Have another turn each.

In class How good are the children at drawing shapes? Are all the shapes intended to be regular?

Cylinders

A person to talk to

Look around your home. Find an example of a cylinder. Stand it on its end and draw round it.

If possible, bring it and the drawing into school.

In class Discuss the shapes of the cylinders. Discuss the shape they get when they draw round the end face.

Above and below

A person to talk to

Look around your home. Find something that is directly above something else.

Draw the 2 things carefully. Label the objects 'above' and 'below'.

In class Discuss the children's different examples. Look around the classroom for other examples.

Symmetrical patterns

One player places 3 counters on their half of the grid.

The other player places 3 counters on their half to make a symmetrical pattern.

Play several times, taking turns to go first.

In class Play this in class, putting the children in pairs.

Blue and white

Ask someone to write these 2 headings.

Look around the room and find things that fit under each heading.

Draw or write each thing under its heading.

 blue

 white

In class Make a class list of all the things they found at home.

Straight and curved

A person to help you

Ask someone to help you copy these 3 headings.

Write at least 2 numbers under each heading.

straight lines	curved lines	straight and curved lines
7	**6**	**5**

In class Put the lists on the board and go through the numbers together, with the children suggesting where each should go.

Sandwich fillings

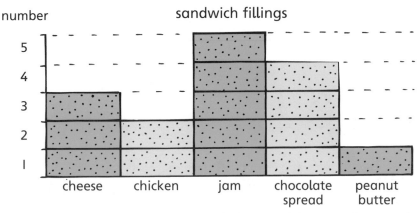

number   sandwich fillings

The graph shows how many children like each sandwich filling best. Answer these questions:

1   How many children like cheese best?

2   Which filling is the most popular?

3   Which filling is the least popular?

4   How many more children like chocolate spread than like jam?

In class Make a class graph of their preferred sandwich fillings.

Favourite footwear

Look at the pictograph.
Answer these questions.

favourite shoes

trainers	👟	👟	👟	👟	👟
sandals	👟				
slippers	👟	👟	👟		
lace-ups	👟				
boots	👟	👟	👟		

1 Which shoes are most children's favourites?

2 Which shoes are fewest children's favourites?

3 How many children like sandals best?

4 How many children like trainers best?

5 How many more children chose trainers than boots?

6 How many more children chose slippers than lace-ups?

In class Discuss their answers. Make a class graph of their favourite footwear.

Clothes show

black	blue	red	green	yellow	white	orange
			jersey	T-shirt		
			skirt			

Copy this table. Write the names, or draw as many articles of your clothing as possible in the table, in the correct column.

In class Make a large version of this table with all children's favourite clothes on it.